Gratitude Journal

D1115787

Invest few minutes a day to develop thankfulness,
mindfulness and positivity

90 Days of daily practice to cultivate happiness

Hi!

My name is Sujatha Lalgudi.
Thank you for purchasing this book.

I hope you find this journal to be helpful in your journey of gratitude and happiness and will continue the practice…

Write to me at **sujatha.lalgudi@gmail.com** with the subject as **Gratitude** to get free printable coloring pages to practice mindfulness & relaxation.

If you liked this book, please leave me a review on Amazon! Your kind reviews and comments will encourage me to make more journals like this.

Thank you
Sujatha Lalgudi

Affirmations

My potential to succeed is infinite.
I take pride in the progress I make each day.
I am proud of myself and all that I have accomplished.
I respect and treat myself with kindness and love.
People like me, and I feel good about myself.
The world is a better place with me in it.
I go for goals with passion and pride.
I am never a burden.
I am worthy of greatness.
I am smart, capable and valuable.
I am at peace with myself.
I accept myself as I am.
I am unique in my own wonderful way.
I am focused, persistent and will never quit.
I am in charge of my own happiness.
I have the power to create change.
I take pride in my achievements.
I have courage and confidence.
I can get through anything.
I don't need to be perfect.
I am an amazing person.
I love myself.
I can do anything.
I can make a difference.
I am in charge of my life.
I set goals and I reach them.
Today, I will walk through my fears.
I am proud of my own success.
I celebrate my individuality.
I am my own superhero.
I am free to be myself.
I trust myself.
I am enough.
I am whole.
I live each day to the fullest.

My Goals/Thoughts/Plans for the next 90 days

Make Gratitude your new habit

As you practice your new habit each day,

Celebrate your progress and check off each day of your efforts!

Week 1	1	2	3	4	5	6	7	1
Week 2	8	9	10	11	12	13	14	2
Week 3	15	16	17	18	19	20	21	3
Week 4	22	23	24	25	26	27	28	4
Week 5	29	30	31	32	33	34	35	5
Week 6	36	37	38	39	40	41	42	6
Week 7	43	44	45	46	47	48	49	7
Week 8	50	51	52	53	54	55	56	8
Week 9	57	58	59	60	61	62	63	9
Week 10	64	65	66	67	68	69	70	10
Week 11	71	72	73	74	75	76	77	11
Week 12	78	79	80	81	82	83	84	12
Week 13	85	86	87	88	89	90		13

My Monthly Plans:

"You must be the change you wish to see in the world."
– Mahatma Gandhi

Goals I envision:

_____

_____

_____

Improvements I seek:

_____

_____

_____

Notes:

_____

_____

_____

Today, I am grateful for: Date: _____

_____

_____

_____

How will I make today awesome?

_____

_____

_____

Positive affirmations:

_____

_____

_____

"We are what we repeatedly do.
Excellence, then, is not an act, but a habit."
– Aristotle

Little things that made my day:

_____

_____

_____

Learning(s) from today:

_____

_____

_____

Goals/Plans for Tomorrow: I am feeling:

_____

_____   ☺ 😐 ☹

Today, I am grateful for: Date: _____

_____

_____

_____

How will I make today awesome?

_____

_____

_____

Positive affirmations:

_____

_____

_____

"Learn to be thankful for what you already have,
while you pursue all that you want."
– Jim Rohn

Little things that made my day:

_____

_____

_____

Learning(s) from today:

_____

_____

_____

Goals/Plans for Tomorrow: I am feeling:

_____

_____   ☺ 😐 ☹

Today, I am grateful for: Date: _____

_____
_____
_____

How will I make today awesome?

_____
_____
_____

Positive affirmations:

_____
_____
_____

"Each morning we are born again.
What we do today is what matters most."
– Buddha

Little things that made my day:

_____
_____
_____

Learning(s) from today:

_____
_____
_____

Goals/Plans for Tomorrow: I am feeling:

_____
_____   ☺   😐   ☹

Today, I am grateful for: Date: _____

_____

_____

_____

How will I make today awesome?

_____

_____

_____

Positive affirmations:

_____

_____

_____

"Make each day your masterpiece."
– John Wooden

Little things that made my day:

_____

_____

_____

Learning(s) from today:

_____

_____

_____

Goals/Plans for Tomorrow: I am feeling:

_____

_____   😊 😐 🙁

Today, I am grateful for: Date: _____

_____
_____
_____

How will I make today awesome?

_____
_____
_____

Positive affirmations:

_____
_____
_____

*"Give every day the chance to become
the most beautiful day of your life."*
– Mark Twain

Little things that made my day:

_____
_____
_____

Learning(s) from today:

_____
_____
_____

Goals/Plans for Tomorrow: I am feeling:

_____
_____   😊 😐 ☹️

Today, I am grateful for: Date: _____

_____
_____
_____

How will I make today awesome?

_____
_____

Positive affirmations:

_____
_____
_____

"Action is the foundational key to all success."
– Pablo Picasso

Little things that made my day:

_____
_____
_____

Learning(s) from today:

_____
_____
_____

Goals/Plans for Tomorrow: I am feeling:

_____
_____   ☺ 😐 ☹

Today, I am grateful for: Date: _____

_____

_____

_____

How will I make today awesome?

_____

_____

_____

Positive affirmations:

_____

_____

_____

"Someday is not a day of the week."
– Denise Brennan-Nelson

Little things that made my day:

_____

_____

_____

Learning(s) from today:

_____

_____

_____

Goals/Plans for Tomorrow: I am feeling:

_____

_____   ☺ 😐 ☹

Today, I am grateful for: Date: _____

_____
_____
_____

How will I make today awesome?

_____
_____
_____

Positive affirmations:

_____
_____
_____

"Success occurs when opportunity meets preparation."
– Zig Ziglar

Little things that made my day:

_____
_____
_____

Learning(s) from today:

_____
_____
_____

Goals/Plans for Tomorrow: I am feeling:

_____
_____   :) :| :(

Today, I am grateful for: Date: _____

_____

_____

_____

How will I make today awesome?

_____

_____

_____

Positive affirmations:

_____

_____

_____

"The best dreams happen when you're awake."
– Cherie Gilderbloom

Little things that made my day:

_____

_____

_____

Learning(s) from today:

_____

_____

_____

Goals/Plans for Tomorrow: I am feeling:

_____

_____   ☺ 😐 ☹

Today, I am grateful for: Date: _____

_____

_____

_____

How will I make today awesome?

_____

_____

_____

Positive affirmations:

_____

_____

_____

"Don't count the days, make the days count."
– Muhammad Ali

Little things that made my day:

_____

_____

_____

Learning(s) from today:

_____

_____

_____

Goals/Plans for Tomorrow: I am feeling:

_____   ☺ 😐 ☹

Today, I am grateful for: Date: _____

_____

_____

_____

How will I make today awesome?

_____

_____

Positive affirmations:

_____

_____

_____

"The difference between ordinary and
extraordinary is that little extra."
– Jimmy Johnson

Little things that made my day:

_____

_____

_____

Learning(s) from today:

_____

_____

_____

Goals/Plans for Tomorrow: I am feeling:

_____

_____   🙂 😐 🙁

Today, I am grateful for: Date: _____

_____

_____

_____

How will I make today awesome?

_____

_____

_____

Positive affirmations:

_____

_____

_____

"It's time to start living the life you've imagined
– Henry James

Little things that made my day:

_____

_____

_____

Learning(s) from today:

_____

_____

_____

Goals/Plans for Tomorrow: I am feeling:

_____

_____   :) :| :(

Today, I am grateful for: Date: _____

_____

_____

_____

How will I make today awesome?

_____

_____

_____

Positive affirmations:

_____

_____

_____

"If there is no struggle, there is no progress."
– Frederick Douglass

Little things that made my day:

_____

_____

_____

Learning(s) from today:

_____

_____

_____

Goals/Plans for Tomorrow: I am feeling:

_____

_____   ☺ 😐 ☹

Today, I am grateful for:

Date: _____

_____

_____

_____

How will I make today awesome?

_____

_____

_____

Positive affirmations:

_____

_____

_____

"The more I want to get something done,
the less I call it work."
– Richard Bach

Little things that made my day:

_____

_____

_____

Learning(s) from today:

_____

_____

_____

Goals/Plans for Tomorrow:

I am feeling:

_____

😊　😐　🙁

Today, I am grateful for: Date: _____

_____

_____

_____

How will I make today awesome?

_____

_____

_____

Positive affirmations:

_____

_____

_____

"My future starts when I wake up every morning."
– Miles Davis

Little things that made my day:

_____

_____

_____

Learning(s) from today:

_____

_____

_____

Goals/Plans for Tomorrow: I am feeling:

_____

_____   :) :| :(

Today, I am grateful for: Date: _____

_____

_____

_____

How will I make today awesome?

_____

_____

_____

Positive affirmations:

_____

_____

_____

"A year from now you may wish you had started today."
– Karen Lamb

Little things that made my day:

_____

_____

_____

Learning(s) from today:

_____

_____

_____

Goals/Plans for Tomorrow: I am feeling:

_____   ☺ 😐 ☹

_____

Today, I am grateful for: Date: _____

_____

_____

_____

How will I make today awesome?

_____

_____

_____

Positive affirmations:

_____

_____

_____

"Be willing to be a beginner every single morning."
– Meister Eckhart

Little things that made my day:

_____

_____

_____

Learning(s) from today:

_____

_____

_____

Goals/Plans for Tomorrow: I am feeling:

_____

_____   😊 😐 🙁

Today, I am grateful for: Date: _____

_____

_____

_____

How will I make today awesome?

_____

_____

_____

Positive affirmations:

_____

_____

_____

"If you aren't going all the way, why go at all?"
– Joe Namath

Little things that made my day:

_____

_____

_____

Learning(s) from today:

_____

_____

_____

Goals/Plans for Tomorrow: I am feeling:

_____

_____   😊 😐 ☹️

Today, I am grateful for: Date: _____

_____

_____

_____

How will I make today awesome?

_____

_____

_____

Positive affirmations:

_____

_____

_____

"Become the person who would
attract the results you seek."
– Jim Cathcart

Little things that made my day:

_____

_____

_____

Learning(s) from today:

_____

_____

_____

Goals/Plans for Tomorrow: I am feeling:

_____

    😊   😐   🙁

Today, I am grateful for: Date: _____

_____
_____
_____

How will I make today awesome?

_____
_____
_____

Positive affirmations:

_____
_____
_____

"Act as if what you do makes a difference.
It does."
– William James

Little things that made my day:

_____
_____
_____

Learning(s) from today:

_____
_____
_____

Goals/Plans for Tomorrow: I am feeling:

_____   ☺ 😐 ☹
_____

Today, I am grateful for: Date: _____

_____
_____
_____

How will I make today awesome?

_____
_____
_____

Positive affirmations:

_____
_____
_____

"Begin by always expecting good things to happen."
– Tom Hopkins

Little things that made my day:

_____
_____
_____

Learning(s) from today:

_____
_____
_____

Goals/Plans for Tomorrow: I am feeling:

_____
_____   ☺ 😐 ☹

Today, I am grateful for:　　　　　　　　Date: _____

_____

_____

_____

How will I make today awesome?

_____

_____

_____

Positive affirmations:

_____

_____

_____

"Don't be pushed by your problems.
Be led by your dreams."
– Ralph Waldo Emerson

Little things that made my day:

_____

_____

_____

Learning(s) from today:

_____

_____

_____

Goals/Plans for Tomorrow:　　　　　　　　I am feeling:

_____

_____　　😊　😐　☹️

Today, I am grateful for: Date: _____

_____

_____

_____

How will I make today awesome?

_____

_____

_____

Positive affirmations:

_____

_____

_____

""Don't watch the clock; do what it does.
Keep going."
– Sam Levenson

Little things that made my day:

_____

_____

_____

Learning(s) from today:

_____

_____

_____

Goals/Plans for Tomorrow: I am feeling:

_____

_____   ☺   😐   ☹

Today, I am grateful for:　　　　　　　　　Date: _____

_____

_____

_____

How will I make today awesome?

_____

_____

_____

Positive affirmations:

_____

_____

_____

"The harder I work, the luckier I get."
– Gary Player

Little things that made my day:

_____

_____

_____

Learning(s) from today:

_____

_____

_____

Goals/Plans for Tomorrow:　　　　　　　　　I am feeling:

_____

_____　　　😊　😐　☹️

Today, I am grateful for: Date: _____

_____
_____
_____

How will I make today awesome?

_____
_____

Positive affirmations:

_____
_____
_____

"You are what you do, not what you say you'll do."
– C.G. Jung

Little things that made my day:

_____
_____
_____

Learning(s) from today:

_____
_____
_____

Goals/Plans for Tomorrow: I am feeling:

_____
_____   😊 😐 🙁

Today, I am grateful for: Date: _____

_____

_____

_____

How will I make today awesome?

_____

_____

Positive affirmations:

_____

_____

_____

"The purpose of our lives is to be happy."
– Dalai Lama

Little things that made my day:

_____

_____

_____

Learning(s) from today:

_____

_____

_____

Goals/Plans for Tomorrow: I am feeling:

_____

_____   😊 😐 😟

Today, I am grateful for: Date: _____

_____

_____

_____

How will I make today awesome?

_____

_____

_____

Positive affirmations:

_____

_____

_____

"Change your thoughts and you change your world."
– Norman Vincent Peale

Little things that made my day:

_____

_____

_____

Learning(s) from today:

_____

_____

_____

Goals/Plans for Tomorrow: I am feeling:

_____

_____   ☺ 😐 ☹

Today, I am grateful for: Date: _____

_____

_____

_____

How will I make today awesome?

_____

_____

_____

Positive affirmations:

_____

_____

_____

"Well done is better than well said."
– Benjamin Franklin

Little things that made my day:

_____

_____

_____

Learning(s) from today:

_____

_____

_____

Goals/Plans for Tomorrow: I am feeling:

_____   😊 😐 🙁

_____

Today, I am grateful for: Date: _____

_____
_____
_____

How will I make today awesome?

_____
_____
_____

Positive affirmations:

_____
_____
_____

"Don't wait. The time will never be just right."
– Napoleon Hill

Little things that made my day:

_____
_____
_____

Learning(s) from today:

_____
_____
_____

Goals/Plans for Tomorrow: I am feeling:

_____
_____   :)   :| :(

Today, I am grateful for: Date: _____

_____

_____

_____

How will I make today awesome?

_____

_____

_____

Positive affirmations:

_____

_____

_____

"The best way out is always through."
– Robert Frost

Little things that made my day:

_____

_____

_____

Learning(s) from today:

_____

_____

_____

Goals/Plans for Tomorrow: I am feeling:

_____   ☺ 😐 ☹

_____

Monthly Reflection:

Looking back:

Wins:

_____

_____

_____

Distractions: Excuses:

_____   _____

_____   _____

_____   _____

"The aim of an argument or discussion
should not be victory, but progress."
– Joseph Joubert

Looking ahead:

Goals:

_____

_____

_____

Improvements:

_____

_____

_____

Notes:

_____

_____

_____

Today, I am grateful for: Date: _____

_____

_____

_____

How will I make today awesome?

_____

_____

Positive affirmations:

_____

_____

_____

"Do one thing each day that scares you."
– Eleanor Roosevelt

Little things that made my day:

_____

_____

_____

Learning(s) from today:

_____

_____

_____

Goals/Plans for Tomorrow: I am feeling:

_____

_____   ☺   😐   ☹

Today, I am grateful for: Date: _____

_____
_____
_____

How will I make today awesome?

_____
_____
_____

Positive affirmations:

_____
_____
_____

Success is the sum of small efforts,
repeated day in and day out.
– Robert Collier

Little things that made my day:

_____
_____
_____

Learning(s) from today:

_____
_____
_____

Goals/Plans for Tomorrow: I am feeling:

_____
_____   ☺ 😐 ☹

Today, I am grateful for: Date: _____

_____
_____
_____

How will I make today awesome?

_____
_____
_____

Positive affirmations:

_____
_____
_____

"You're only limit is you."
– Unknown

Little things that made my day:

_____
_____
_____

Learning(s) from today:

_____
_____
_____

Goals/Plans for Tomorrow: I am feeling:

_____
_____   ☺ 😐 ☹

Today, I am grateful for: Date: _____

_____

_____

_____

How will I make today awesome?

_____

_____

_____

Positive affirmations:

_____

_____

_____

"Wherever you are, be all there."
– Jim Elliot

Little things that made my day:

_____

_____

_____

Learning(s) from today:

_____

_____

_____

Goals/Plans for Tomorrow: I am feeling:

_____

_____   😊 😐 ☹️

Today, I am grateful for:　　　　　　　　Date: _____

_____

_____

_____

How will I make today awesome?

_____

_____

_____

Positive affirmations:

_____

_____

_____

*"Your imagination is your preview of
life's coming attractions."
— Albert Einstein*

Little things that made my day:

_____

_____

_____

Learning(s) from today:

_____

_____

_____

Goals/Plans for Tomorrow:　　　　　　　　I am feeling:

_____

_____　　😊　😐　☹️

Today, I am grateful for: Date: _____

_____
_____
_____

How will I make today awesome?

_____
_____
_____

Positive affirmations:

_____
_____
_____

*"It often takes more courage to change
one's opinion than to keep it."*
– Willy Brandt

Little things that made my day:

_____
_____
_____

Learning(s) from today:

_____
_____
_____

Goals/Plans for Tomorrow: I am feeling:

_____
_____   ☺ ☺ ☹

Today, I am grateful for: Date: _____

_____

_____

_____

How will I make today awesome?

_____

_____

_____

Positive affirmations:

_____

_____

_____

"Inspiration does exist, but it must find you working."
– Pablo Picasso

Little things that made my day:

_____

_____

_____

Learning(s) from today:

_____

_____

_____

Goals/Plans for Tomorrow: I am feeling:

_____

_____   :) :| :(

Today, I am grateful for: Date: _____

_____

_____

_____

How will I make today awesome?

_____

_____

_____

Positive affirmations:

_____

_____

_____

"If you try, you risk failure.
If you don't, you ensure it."
– Anonymous

Little things that made my day:

_____

_____

_____

Learning(s) from today:

_____

_____

_____

Goals/Plans for Tomorrow: I am feeling:

_____

_____   ☺ 😐 ☹

Today, I am grateful for: Date: _____

_____

_____

_____

How will I make today awesome?

_____

_____

_____

Positive affirmations:

_____

_____

_____

*"Setting goals is the first step in turning
the invisible into the visible."
– Tony Robbins*

Little things that made my day:

_____

_____

_____

Learning(s) from today:

_____

_____

_____

Goals/Plans for Tomorrow: I am feeling:

_____

_____   😊   😐   🙁

Today, I am grateful for: Date: _____

_____

_____

_____

How will I make today awesome?

_____

_____

_____

Positive affirmations:

_____

_____

_____

"The harder the conflict, the more glorious the triumph."
– Thomas Paine

Little things that made my day:

_____

_____

_____

Learning(s) from today:

_____

_____

_____

Goals/Plans for Tomorrow: I am feeling:

_____

_____   😊   😐   🙁

Today, I am grateful for: Date: _____

_____

_____

_____

How will I make today awesome?

_____

_____

Positive affirmations:

_____

_____

_____

"Your attitude, not your aptitude,
will determine your altitude."
– Zig Ziglar

Little things that made my day:

_____

_____

_____

Learning(s) from today:

_____

_____

_____

Goals/Plans for Tomorrow: I am feeling:

_____

_____   ☺ 😐 ☹

Today, I am grateful for: Date: _____

_____

_____

_____

How will I make today awesome?

_____

_____

Positive affirmations:

_____

_____

_____

"What we dwell on is who we become."
– Oprah Winfrey

Little things that made my day:

_____

_____

_____

Learning(s) from today:

_____

_____

_____

Goals/Plans for Tomorrow: I am feeling:

_____

_____   ☺ 😐 ☹

Today, I am grateful for: Date: _____

_____

_____

_____

How will I make today awesome?

_____

_____

_____

Positive affirmations:

_____

_____

_____

"It is well to be up before daybreak, for such habits
contribute to health, wealth, and wisdom."
– Aristotle

Little things that made my day:

_____

_____

_____

Learning(s) from today:

_____

_____

_____

Goals/Plans for Tomorrow: I am feeling:

_____

_____   ☺   😐   ☹

Today, I am grateful for:

Date: _____

How will I make today awesome?

Positive affirmations:

*"You must not only aim right, but draw the bow
with all your might."
– Henry David Thoreau*

Little things that made my day:

Learning(s) from today:

Goals/Plans for Tomorrow:

I am feeling:

😊 😐 🙁

Today, I am grateful for: Date: _____

_____

_____

_____

How will I make today awesome?

_____

_____

_____

Positive affirmations:

_____

_____

_____

*"Don't worry about failures, worry about
the chances you miss when you don't even try."*
– Jack Canfield

Little things that made my day:

_____

_____

_____

Learning(s) from today:

_____

_____

_____

Goals/Plans for Tomorrow: I am feeling:

_____   ☺   😐   ☹

Today, I am grateful for: Date: _____

_____

_____

_____

How will I make today awesome?

_____

_____

_____

Positive affirmations:

_____

_____

_____

"Though no one can go back and make a brand new start,
anyone can start from now and make a brand new ending."
– Carl Bard

Little things that made my day:

_____

_____

_____

Learning(s) from today:

_____

_____

_____

Goals/Plans for Tomorrow: I am feeling:

_____

_____   ☺ 😐 ☹

Today, I am grateful for: Date:

_____

_____

_____

How will I make today awesome?

_____

_____

_____

Positive affirmations:

_____

_____

_____

"An obstacle is often a stepping stone."
– William Prescott

Little things that made my day:

_____

_____

_____

Learning(s) from today:

_____

_____

_____

Goals/Plans for Tomorrow: I am feeling:

_____

_____   ☺ 😐 ☹

Today, I am grateful for: Date: _____

_____

_____

_____

How will I make today awesome?

_____

_____

_____

Positive affirmations:

_____

_____

_____

*"Never give up on something that you can't go
a day without thinking about."*
– Unknown

Little things that made my day:

_____

_____

_____

Learning(s) from today:

_____

_____

_____

Goals/Plans for Tomorrow: I am feeling:

_____

_____   ☺ 😐 ☹

Today, I am grateful for: Date: _____

_____

_____

_____

How will I make today awesome?

_____

_____

_____

Positive affirmations:

_____

_____

_____

"Keep your face to the sunshine
and you can never see the shadow."
– Helen Keller

Little things that made my day:

_____

_____

_____

Learning(s) from today:

_____

_____

_____

Goals/Plans for Tomorrow: I am feeling:

_____   😊 😐 🙁

Today, I am grateful for:　　　　　　　Date: _____

_____

_____

_____

How will I make today awesome?

_____

_____

_____

Positive affirmations:

_____

_____

_____

"When you arise in the morning, think of what a precious privilege
it is to be alive – to breathe, to think, to enjoy, to love."
– Marcus Aurelius

Little things that made my day:

_____

_____

_____

Learning(s) from today:

_____

_____

_____

Goals/Plans for Tomorrow:　　　　　　　I am feeling:

_____

_____　　😊　😐　🙁

Today, I am grateful for:

Date: _____

_____

_____

_____

How will I make today awesome?

_____

_____

_____

Positive affirmations:

_____

_____

_____

"Every day may not be good,
but there's something good in every day."
– Alice Morse Earle

Little things that made my day:

_____

_____

_____

Learning(s) from today:

_____

_____

_____

Goals/Plans for Tomorrow:

I am feeling:

_____

_____

☺ ☻ ☹

Today, I am grateful for: Date: _____

_____

_____

_____

How will I make today awesome?

_____

_____

_____

Positive affirmations:

_____

_____

_____

"It's not about having the right opportunities.
It's about handling the opportunities right."
– Mark Hunter

Little things that made my day:

_____

_____

_____

Learning(s) from today:

_____

_____

_____

Goals/Plans for Tomorrow: I am feeling:

_____

_____   ☺ 😐 ☹

Today, I am grateful for: Date: _____

_____
_____
_____

How will I make today awesome?

_____
_____
_____

Positive affirmations:

_____
_____
_____

"Happiness is not something readymade.
It comes from your own actions." – Dalai Lama

Little things that made my day:

_____
_____
_____

Learning(s) from today:

_____
_____
_____

Goals/Plans for Tomorrow: I am feeling:

_____
_____   ☺ 😐 ☹

Today, I am grateful for: Date: _____

_____

_____

_____

How will I make today awesome?

_____

_____

_____

Positive affirmations:

_____

_____

_____

"What you do speaks so loudly that I cannot hear what you say."
– Ralph Waldo Emerson

Little things that made my day:

_____

_____

_____

Learning(s) from today:

_____

_____

_____

Goals/Plans for Tomorrow: I am feeling:

_____

_____   😊   😐   🙁

Today, I am grateful for: Date: _____

_____

_____

_____

How will I make today awesome?

_____

_____

_____

Positive affirmations:

_____

_____

_____

"Tough times never last, but tough people do."
– Dr. Robert Schuller

Little things that made my day:

_____

_____

_____

Learning(s) from today:

_____

_____

_____

Goals/Plans for Tomorrow: I am feeling:

_____

_____   ☺ 😐 ☹

Today, I am grateful for: Date: _____

_____

_____

_____

How will I make today awesome?

_____

_____

_____

Positive affirmations:

_____

_____

_____

""I simply wake up every morning a better person
than when I went to bed."
– Sidney Poitier

Little things that made my day:

_____

_____

_____

Learning(s) from today:

_____

_____

_____

Goals/Plans for Tomorrow: I am feeling:

_____

_____   😊 😐 🙁

Today, I am grateful for: Date: _____

_____

_____

_____

How will I make today awesome?

_____

_____

_____

Positive affirmations:

_____

_____

_____

*"I'm going to make everything around me beautiful
– that will be my life."*
– Elsie De Wolfe

Little things that made my day:

_____

_____

_____

Learning(s) from today:

_____

_____

_____

Goals/Plans for Tomorrow: I am feeling:

_____

_____ 😊 😐 🙁

Today, I am grateful for: Date: _____

_____

_____

_____

How will I make today awesome?

_____

_____

_____

Positive affirmations:

_____

_____

_____

"All our dreams can come true –
if we have the courage to pursue them."
– Walt Disney

Little things that made my day:

_____

_____

_____

Learning(s) from today:

_____

_____

_____

Goals/Plans for Tomorrow: I am feeling:

_____   😊 😐 ☹️

_____

Today, I am grateful for:　　　　　　Date: _____

_____

_____

_____

How will I make today awesome?

_____

_____

_____

Positive affirmations:

_____

_____

_____

"The best way to predict the future is to invent it."
– Alan Kay

Little things that made my day:

_____

_____

_____

Learning(s) from today:

_____

_____

_____

Goals/Plans for Tomorrow:　　　　　　I am feeling:

_____

_____ 　😊　😐　🙁

Today, I am grateful for:
Date: _____

_____
_____
_____

How will I make today awesome?

_____
_____
_____

Positive affirmations:

_____
_____
_____

The future depends on what you do today.
— Mahatma Gandhi

Little things that made my day:

_____
_____
_____

Learning(s) from today:

_____
_____
_____

Goals/Plans for Tomorrow:
I am feeling:

_____
_____

😊 😐 🙁

Monthly Reflection:

Looking back:

Wins:

_____

_____

_____

Distractions: Excuses:

_____   _____

_____   _____

_____   _____

"Every strike brings me closer to the next home run."
– Babe Ruth

Looking ahead:

Goals:

_____

_____

_____

Improvements:

_____

_____

_____

Notes:

_____

_____

_____

Today, I am grateful for: Date: _____

_____
_____
_____

How will I make today awesome?

_____
_____
_____

Positive affirmations:

_____
_____
_____

"Treat objections as requests for further information."
– Brian Tracy

Little things that made my day:

_____
_____
_____

Learning(s) from today:

_____
_____
_____

Goals/Plans for Tomorrow: I am feeling:

_____
_____   🙂 😐 🙁

Today, I am grateful for: Date: _____

_____

_____

_____

How will I make today awesome?

_____

_____

_____

Positive affirmations:

_____

_____

_____

"Courage is never to let your actions be influenced by your fears."
– Arthur Koestler

Little things that made my day:

_____

_____

_____

Learning(s) from today:

_____

_____

_____

Goals/Plans for Tomorrow: I am feeling:

_____

_____   ☺ 😐 ☹

Today, I am grateful for: Date: _____

_____

_____

_____

How will I make today awesome?

_____

_____

_____

Positive affirmations:

_____

_____

_____

"We are what our thoughts have made us; so take care about what
you think. Words are secondary. Thoughts live; they travel far."
– Swami Vivekananda

Little things that made my day:

_____

_____

_____

Learning(s) from today:

_____

_____

_____

Goals/Plans for Tomorrow: I am feeling:

_____

_____   ☺ 😐 ☹

Today, I am grateful for: Date: _____

_____

_____

_____

How will I make today awesome?

_____

_____

_____

Positive affirmations:

_____

_____

_____

"Whether you think you can or you can't, you're right."
– Henry Ford

Little things that made my day:

_____

_____

_____

Learning(s) from today:

_____

_____

_____

Goals/Plans for Tomorrow: I am feeling:

_____

_____   😊 😐 ☹️

Today, I am grateful for: Date: _____

_____

_____

_____

How will I make today awesome?

_____

_____

_____

Positive affirmations:

_____

_____

_____

"Don't judge each day by the harvest you reap
but by the seeds that you plant."
– Robert Louis Stevenson

Little things that made my day:

_____

_____

_____

Learning(s) from today:

_____

_____

_____

Goals/Plans for Tomorrow: I am feeling:

_____

_____   😊 😐 ☹️

Today, I am grateful for: Date: _____

_____

_____

How will I make today awesome?

_____

_____

Positive affirmations:

_____

_____

_____

"To live is the rarest thing in the world.
Most people exist, that is all."
– Oscar Wilde

Little things that made my day:

_____

_____

_____

Learning(s) from today:

_____

_____

_____

Goals/Plans for Tomorrow: I am feeling:

_____

_____   ☺ 😐 ☹

Today, I am grateful for: Date: _____

_____
_____
_____

How will I make today awesome?

_____
_____
_____

Positive affirmations:

_____
_____
_____

*"Only those who will risk going too far
can possibly find out how far one can go."*
– T.S. Eliot

Little things that made my day:

_____
_____
_____

Learning(s) from today:

_____
_____
_____

Goals/Plans for Tomorrow: I am feeling:

_____   ☺ 😐 ☹
_____

Today, I am grateful for:

Date: _____

How will I make today awesome?

Positive affirmations:

"Just keep going. Everybody gets better if they keep at it."
– Ted Williams

Little things that made my day:

Learning(s) from today:

Goals/Plans for Tomorrow:

I am feeling:

☺ ☺ ☹

Today, I am grateful for: Date: _____

_____
_____
_____

How will I make today awesome?

_____
_____
_____

Positive affirmations:

_____
_____
_____

"It is never too late to be what you might have been."
– George Eliot

Little things that made my day:

_____
_____
_____

Learning(s) from today:

_____
_____
_____

Goals/Plans for Tomorrow: I am feeling:

_____
_____   ☺ 😐 ☹

Today, I am grateful for: Date: _____

_____

_____

_____

How will I make today awesome?

_____

_____

_____

Positive affirmations:

_____

_____

_____

"Don't wish it were easier, wish you were better."
– Jim Rohn

Little things that made my day:

_____

_____

_____

Learning(s) from today:

_____

_____

_____

Goals/Plans for Tomorrow: I am feeling:

_____   😊 😐 ☹️

_____

Today, I am grateful for: Date: _____

_____

_____

_____

How will I make today awesome?

_____

_____

_____

Positive affirmations:

_____

_____

_____

"Never let your memories be greater than your dreams."
– Doug Ivester

Little things that made my day:

_____

_____

_____

Learning(s) from today:

_____

_____

_____

Goals/Plans for Tomorrow: I am feeling:

_____

_____   ☺ 😐 ☹

Today, I am grateful for: Date: _____

_____

_____

_____

How will I make today awesome?

_____

_____

Positive affirmations:

_____

_____

_____

*"Nothing important was ever achieved
without someone taking a chance."*
– H. Jackson Brown, Jr

Little things that made my day:

_____

_____

_____

Learning(s) from today:

_____

_____

_____

Goals/Plans for Tomorrow: I am feeling:

_____   😊 😐 ☹️

_____

Today, I am grateful for: Date: _____

_____
_____
_____

How will I make today awesome?

_____
_____
_____

Positive affirmations:

_____
_____
_____

*"There are two primary choices in life: to accept conditions
as they exist, or accept the responsibility for changing them."*
– Denis Waitley

Little things that made my day:

_____
_____
_____

Learning(s) from today:

_____
_____
_____

Goals/Plans for Tomorrow: I am feeling:

_____   ☺ 😐 ☹
_____

Today, I am grateful for: Date: _____

_____

_____

_____

How will I make today awesome?

_____

_____

_____

Positive affirmations:

_____

_____

_____

*"In three words I can sum up everything
I've learned about life: It goes on."
– Robert Frost*

Little things that made my day:

_____

_____

_____

Learning(s) from today:

_____

_____

_____

Goals/Plans for Tomorrow: I am feeling:

_____

_____   😊   😐   🙁

Today, I am grateful for: Date: _____

_____
_____
_____

How will I make today awesome?

_____
_____
_____

Positive affirmations:

_____
_____
_____

"If you aim at nothing, you will hit it every time."
– Zig Ziglar

Little things that made my day:

_____
_____
_____

Learning(s) from today:

_____
_____
_____

Goals/Plans for Tomorrow: I am feeling:

_____
_____   🙂 😐 🙁

Today, I am grateful for: Date: _____

_____

_____

_____

How will I make today awesome?

_____

_____

_____

Positive affirmations:

_____

_____

_____

"If you're offered a seat on a rocket ship,
don't ask what seat! Just get on."
– Sheryl Sandberg

Little things that made my day:

_____

_____

_____

Learning(s) from today:

_____

_____

_____

Goals/Plans for Tomorrow: I am feeling:

_____

_____   ☺ 😐 ☹

Today, I am grateful for: Date: _____

_____

_____

_____

How will I make today awesome?

_____

_____

_____

Positive affirmations:

_____

_____

_____

"People often say that motivation doesn't last.
Well, neither does bathing. That's why we recommend it daily."
– Zig Ziglar

Little things that made my day:

_____

_____

_____

Learning(s) from today:

_____

_____

_____

Goals/Plans for Tomorrow: I am feeling:

_____

_____   ☺ 😐 ☹

Today, I am grateful for: Date: _____

_____

_____

_____

How will I make today awesome?

_____

_____

_____

Positive affirmations:

_____

_____

_____

"The creation of a thousand forests is in one acorn."
– Ralph Waldo Emerson

Little things that made my day:

_____

_____

_____

Learning(s) from today:

_____

_____

_____

Goals/Plans for Tomorrow: I am feeling:

_____

_____   😊 😐 ☹️

Today, I am grateful for:　　　　　　Date: _____

_____

_____

_____

How will I make today awesome?

_____

_____

_____

Positive affirmations:

_____

_____

_____

"Always be a first-rate version of yourself,
instead of a second-rate version of somebody else."
– Judy Garland

Little things that made my day:

_____

_____

_____

Learning(s) from today:

_____

_____

_____

Goals/Plans for Tomorrow:　　　　　　I am feeling:

_____

_____　　😊　😐　☹️

Today, I am grateful for: Date: _____

_____

_____

_____

How will I make today awesome?

_____

_____

Positive affirmations:

_____

_____

_____

*"Smile in the mirror. Do that every morning and
you'll start to see a big difference in your life."*
– Yoko Ono

Little things that made my day:

_____

_____

_____

Learning(s) from today:

_____

_____

_____

Goals/Plans for Tomorrow: I am feeling:

_____

_____   ☺ 😐 ☹

Today, I am grateful for: Date: _____

_____
_____
_____

How will I make today awesome?

_____
_____
_____

Positive affirmations:

_____
_____
_____

"I am not a product of my circumstances.
I am a product of my decisions."
– Stephen Covey

Little things that made my day:

_____
_____
_____

Learning(s) from today:

_____
_____
_____

Goals/Plans for Tomorrow: I am feeling:

_____
_____   ☺ 😐 ☹

Today, I am grateful for: Date: _____

_____

_____

_____

How will I make today awesome?

_____

_____

_____

Positive affirmations:

_____

_____

_____

"Challenge yourself with something you know you could never do,
and what you'll find is that you can overcome anything."
– Unknown

Little things that made my day:

_____

_____

_____

Learning(s) from today:

_____

_____

_____

Goals/Plans for Tomorrow: I am feeling:

_____

_____   ☺ 😐 ☹

Today, I am grateful for:　　　　　　Date: _____

_____
_____
_____

How will I make today awesome?

_____
_____
_____

Positive affirmations:

_____
_____
_____

"Minds are like parachutes – they only function when open."
– Thomas Dewar

Little things that made my day:

_____
_____
_____

Learning(s) from today:

_____
_____
_____

Goals/Plans for Tomorrow:　　　　　　I am feeling:

_____
_____　　☺ 😐 ☹

Today, I am grateful for: Date:

_____

_____

_____

How will I make today awesome?

_____

_____

Positive affirmations:

_____

_____

_____

"The best way to have a good idea is to have lots of ideas."
– Linus Pauling

Little things that made my day:

_____

_____

_____

Learning(s) from today:

_____

_____

_____

Goals/Plans for Tomorrow: I am feeling:

_____

_____   🙂 😐 🙁

Today, I am grateful for: Date: _____

_____
_____
_____

How will I make today awesome?

_____
_____
_____

Positive affirmations:

_____
_____
_____

"Creativity is the power to connect the seemingly unconnected."
– William Plomer

Little things that made my day:

_____
_____
_____

Learning(s) from today:

_____
_____
_____

Goals/Plans for Tomorrow: I am feeling:

_____
_____   ☺ 😐 ☹

Today, I am grateful for: Date: _____

_____

_____

_____

How will I make today awesome?

_____

_____

_____

Positive affirmations:

_____

_____

_____

"If opportunity doesn't knock, build a door."
– Milton Berle

Little things that made my day:

_____

_____

_____

Learning(s) from today:

_____

_____

_____

Goals/Plans for Tomorrow: I am feeling:

_____

_____   ☺ 😐 ☹

Today, I am grateful for: Date: _____

_____

_____

_____

How will I make today awesome?

_____

_____

_____

Positive affirmations:

_____

_____

_____

"We cannot change the cards we are dealt,
just how we play the hand."
– Randy Pausch

Little things that made my day:

_____

_____

_____

Learning(s) from today:

_____

_____

_____

Goals/Plans for Tomorrow: I am feeling:

_____

☺ 😐 ☹

Today, I am grateful for:

Date: _____

_____

_____

_____

How will I make today awesome?

_____

_____

_____

Positive affirmations:

_____

_____

_____

It is not in the stars to hold our destiny, but in ourselves."
– William Shakespeare

Little things that made my day:

_____

_____

_____

Learning(s) from today:

_____

_____

_____

Goals/Plans for Tomorrow:

I am feeling:

_____

😊 😐 ☹️

Today, I am grateful for: Date: _____

_____

_____

_____

How will I make today awesome?

_____

_____

_____

Positive affirmations:

_____

_____

_____

"When at a conflict between mind and heart,
always follow your heart."
– Swami Vivekananda

Little things that made my day:

_____

_____

_____

Learning(s) from today:

_____

_____

_____

Goals/Plans for Tomorrow: I am feeling:

_____

_____   😊 😐 ☹️

Today, I am grateful for: Date: _____

_____

_____

_____

How will I make today awesome?

_____

_____

_____

Positive affirmations:

_____

_____

_____

"If you cannot do great things, do small things in a great way."
– Napoleon Hill

Little things that made my day:

_____

_____

_____

Learning(s) from today:

_____

_____

_____

Goals/Plans for Tomorrow: I am feeling:

_____

_____   ☺ 😐 ☹

Monthly Reflection:

Date: _____

Looking back:

Wins:

_____

_____

_____

Distractions: Excuses:

_____   _____

_____   _____

_____

"What lies behind us and what lies before us
are tiny matters compared to what lies within us."
– Henry S. Haskins

Looking ahead:

Goals:

_____

_____

_____

Improvements:

_____

_____

_____

Notes:

_____

_____

_____

Be Thankful!

Celebrate your Success!

Share the Joy!

Feel Great Everyday!

Share the joy with kids!
Encourage them to cultivate the
attitude of gratitude:

ISBN: 1696006740

Made in United States
North Haven, CT
13 November 2022

26669531R00059